Table of Contents

D1466024

Optional Items

Heinemann
361 Hanover St.
Portsmouth, NH 03801-3912
www.heinemann.com

Offices and agents throughout the world.

Fountas & Pinnell Benchmark Assessment System 2
Optional Assessment Student Forms

ISBN10 0-325-01265-2
ISBN13 978-0-325-01265-0

Printed in China
3 4 5 6 7 8 NOR 15 14 13 12 11 10 09

Level 4 Word List

silence	plastic
serious	ocean
nature	perform
station	delicious
graceful	pebble
heavy	understood
against	destiny
excuse	future
traffic	anger
reward	honey

Level 5 Word List

speechless	cushion
slumber	population
courage	needle
region	marriage
appearance	obedient
gracious	baggage
honorable	justice
ambition	lately
expression	bushel
protective	lunar

liquid	profitable
reduction	patient
prosperity	tremendous
accustom	patriotic
medicine	compliments
nourishment	spectacular
combination	abundant
wreckage	hostility
rebellion	imaginary
responsible	yearning

continuously	contemporary
environmental	acknowledge
exhausted	malignant
pensive	cubic
society	attentively
approximate	standardize
customary	architecture
reminiscence	industrious
malicious	counterfeit
intricate	recession

boutique	exuberant
meddle	permissive
supplement	inducement
whimsical	exhibition
grotesque	articulate
nonchalant	subtle
contemptuous	granular
antique	succumb
miniature	poignant
simultaneous	rambunctious

100 High-Frequency Words, **page 1**

Read the words:

List 1	List 2	List 3
than	have	over
about	there	ride
back	any	don't
after	into	said
I'm	just	that
been	little	one
big	make	with
came	before	five
away	two	their
your	four	what
who	mother	but
when	where	here
them	very	going
because	could	our
from	were	three

100 High-Frequency Words, **page 2**

Read the words:

List 4		List 5	
want	take	books	sleep
able	dad	good	love
bad	hide	help	much
give	almost	city	stay
today	dog	write	name
week	anything	top	new
something	home	room	paper
bus	down	under	rain
year	become	fast	door
can't	end	hill	fun
tell	behind	know	sky
across	fish	use	both
world	why	let	time
cat	car	place	

200 High-Frequency Words, **page 1**

Read the words:

List 1	List 2	List 3
sea	happy	house
wrote	catch	start
again	third	grew
carry	night	way
wait	goes	friend
each	last	story
feel	school	street
always	walk	above
first	ten	find
ask	change	between
food	outside	every
work	part	should
brother	live	father
through	party	watch
funny	game	children
gave	try	hid
things	pick	enough
close	right	dark
even	teach	great
grow	until	inside
gone	second	light
same	deep	seen
knew	view	during
begin	grade	worm
winter	snow	wrong
must	does	you're
stop	together	

200 High-Frequency Words, **page 2**

Read the words:

List 4		List 5	
several	river	follow	being
never	might	pretty	also
getting	air	couldn't	slowly
earth	I'd	happen	bring
group	suddenly	themselves	hear
baby	easy	direction	often
everything	finally	nothing	page
high	everyone	life	store
wouldn't	hold	someone	while
probably	special	without	however
through	animal	instead	kids
against	lost	either	check
hour	beautiful	lunch	listen
fight	need	important	few
once	job	less	stuff
best	sick	own	problem
ready	maybe	think	such
free	land	round	cleans
show	next	scared	teacher
build	old	person	dream
draw	window	short	sister
state	better	add	plan
kind	written	wanted	they're
circle	favorite	young	possible
large	care	question	thought
doing	myself	yourself	really
family	since	answer	understand
clothes	picture	money	near
hand	class	simple	rest
different	idea	more	soon

Phonograms I Word Lists

List 1	List 2	List 3	List 4
not	shot	ate	chore
man	slam	mane	pile
sit	twig	flake	dive
hen	when	bite	made
pan	drop	sing	smell
day	flap	flame	race
fat	slit	rag	stale
dog	sled	plane	cage
nap	bran	same	stage
tap	ship	drape	sale
pig	shut	plate	space
net	chin	drag	hive
tip	wet	bike	shade
red	plan	white	robe
nut	frog	strike	while
pin	spray	slime	poke
sad	that	tape	spell
rug	plug	bring	bore
hop	glad	rake	choke
jam	flip	dine	bell

© 2008 by Irene C. Fountas and Gay Su Pinnell. Portsmouth, NH: Heinemann. This page may be photocopied.

Phonograms II Word Lists

List 1	List 2
slab	since
shadow	single
stag	slipper
hammer	litter
scan	who
grand	knob
chapter	plod
charter	goggle
splatter	plopped
crawl	spotted
prayer	flowing
fled	flowering
freezing	rubber
blend	druggist
fret	drummer
hidden	stunning
twig	shutter
shimmer	cry

Fountas & Pinnell Benchmark Assessment System 2

Phonograms II Word Lists

List 3		List 4	
grace	dart	thrift	stock
stacked	smash	alike	poke
graded	plate	thrill	folded
flakes	save	grime	sole
scales	bee	twine	crone
fall	smell	fling	spool
blamed	trend	shrink	grope
crane	event	flint	most
slanted	threw	stripe	tote
escape	splice	squish	show
shard	thick	bite	blunt
stark	stride	probe	crush

Phonograms II Word Lists

List 5		List 6	
pact		thrust	
afraid	wrath	cloak	cooking
frail	adapt	shoat	spool
train	teacher	peeled	wool
flair	bread	spleen	spoon
walker	streak	steeped	ignore
cramped	stream	fleet	scorn
danced	cheaper	knelt	frost
crank	rear	flesh	around
glare	bleat	crest	about
flask	flecked	blight	scowl
clasping	greedy	wrist	frown
thatching	creek	wrong	stuff

seal	peel
sail	sweet
stain	heat
meal	braid
boat	lean
main	soap
real	train
rain	seen
speak	goat
sheets	neat
float	road
bean	

claw	grief
cows	grow
crawl	house
toe	moon
spoon	snow
new	pout
few	plow
good	spray
gray	thief
book	wood

Vowel Clusters, **Word List 3**

pour	hair
pearl	tier
boar	poor
air	rear
career	floor
your	peer
pier	soar

Grade 2 Word Features List

Directions: Read these words.

Jack's	my	fish
need	loud	I've
tiger	remake	treat
knit	spy	replay
save	fast	know
I'll	comb	banana
umbrella	mule	scrap
hide	with	don't
lamb	we're	apple
dog's	baby	whale

Grade 3 Word Features List

Directions: Read these words.

first	leave	waste
trouble	sunny	we've
bark	untie	remake
passing	homesick	rotten
chair	bird	boy
deer	batter	pie
they'd	corn	driveway
winter	rough	redo
noise	snore	beast
enter	you've	jellyfish